WHERE'S WALLY?
IN OUTER SPACE

MARTIN HANDFORD

WALKER BOOKS
AND SUBSIDIARIES
LONDON • BOSTON • SYDNEY • AUCKLAND

GREETINGS EARTH-DWELLERS!

PACK YOUR PENS AND BLAST OFF WITH ME ON AN ADVENTURE INTO THE DEEPEST, DARKEST DEPTHS OF SPACE. WE'LL VISIT PUZZLING PLANETS, PLAY GRAVITY-BENDING GAMES AND FIND ANSWERS TO COSMIC CONUNDRUMS AS WE GO. ALSO HELP ME FIND THIS SUPER SPECIAL SHINING STAR!

WHEREVER I GO, WOOF, WENDA, WIZARD WHITEBEARD AND ODLAW GO TOO. SEE IF YOU CAN SPOT OUR LOST THINGS SOMEWHERE IN OUTER SPACE!

WALLY'S KEY | WOOF'S BONE | WENDA'S CAMERA | WIZARD WHITEBEARD'S SCROLL | ODLAW'S BINOCULARS

IT'S OUT OF THIS WORLD!

Wally

SPACE MAIL

Whoops! What an intergalactic mailroom mix up!
Match each message to a stamp to find out
who did (and who didn't) send postcards.

TODAY I MET WOOF AND WENDA WAITING WITH ALIENS AT A SPACESHIP STOP. ONE OF THE ALIENS WAS WEARING A RED-BOBBLED HAT — JUST LIKE MINE! WOW! WISH YOU WERE HERE!

WALLY-WATCHERS
WANDERING ABOUT,
PLANET EARTH,
THE UNIVERSE

Zip-zap-swoosh-boing! I cast a magic spell to make a rocket! Can you believe my beard got caught in its antenna and I was carried light years away!

Wally
Walking Here and There,
With a Walking Stick,
Wherever You Are

I'M FEELING BLUE TODAY, AND NOT JUST IN COLOUR. MY BROTHER (HE STICKS HIS TONGUE OUT A LOT!) WON'T TAKE ME TO HIS SPACEBALL MATCH ON PLANET ZOG. CAN YOU MAKE IT HAPPEN?

MAKE A WISH COME TRUE INC.

LUCKY LETTERBOX,

SHOOTING STAR CITY

I SNOOZED IN THE SOLAR HAMMOCK YOU SENT ME AND FLOATED TOO CLOSE TO THE SUN. I'M NOT ORANGE ANY MORE AND MY THREE EYES ARE SORE! OUCH!

MUM

RED STAR STREET,

NEAR THE BLACK HOLE,

BESIDE PLANET WHOOPSY

RIDDLE ME THIS, RIDDLE ME THAT,

I'M SNEAKING ABOUT LIKE A BLACK CYBER CAT.

I HAVE SUNGLASSES AND A MOUSTACHE FOR MY DISGUISE...

TRY TO TRACK DOWN MY (YELLOW AND BLACK) ALIEN ALLIES!

TOP SECRET

NOWHERE,

EVERYWHERE,

PLANET HIDE & SEEK

MORE THINGS TO DO

✳ Copy the five faces you've matched into the blank stamps.

✳ Can you spot three yellow and black alien friends of Odlaw's? Keep your eyes peeled for five more hiding in the rest of this book!

WANDERING LINES

Blue martians like to sleepwalk! How many rows of the same three do you see? A row can only be straight or diagonal, and Odlaw's found one for you!

WORD WORLDS

Gravity has made mayhem of these words!
Read the clues to help you unscramble the letters.

3. Is really big
PSAEC

1. Another word for Alien
RAIR TELXR TEEA RIT SR

2. The size of this is unknown
URE ENVIS

4. Orbits Earth
OM NO

7. Called the "Red Planet"
MS AR

5. Electronic orbiting object
ATSL LEE IA TEE

6. Drives a spacecraft
SAU NAC TOTR

8. Lights up Earth
SN

11. Has a tail
MTO CEE

12. Our galaxy (two words)
AM KY YWYL

9. Star shine
TNW ILE LKE

10. Instrument with glass lenses
SCT LE POL PEE

MORE THINGS TO FIND

✳ Spot a blue martian who is not sleepwalking, but asleep on a rock!

SPACE STATION DUPLICATION

Can you spot ten differences between each pair of scenes?

TELEPORTATION TANGLE

Beam me up! What a tangle! Follow the teleportation rays to find out who's travelling to which spaceship.

MORE THINGS TO DO

* How many books is Wally holding? What space subjects might they be?

STRANGE CREATURE

Put Hungry Growler's face back together again by writing the numbers from 1–6 in the circle beside each strip.

HALF ALIEN, HALF...

What a bunch of crazy looking creatures!
Can you pair up their top and bottom halves?

MORE THINGS TO DO

★ Use a pencil and paper to trace this page, then cut up the characters' top and bottom halves to make new mixed-up creatures!

LIGHTS, CAMERAS, ALIENS

Are these actors or aliens, or acting aliens? It's a mystery!
Can you spot the silhouettes in this silly space film scene?

MORE THINGS TO FIND

- Four film set cameras
- Forty-eight astronauts
- A space sandcastle
- Five ray guns
- A "loud speaker"

13

TIME AND SPACE MAZE

Find the yellow rocket a route to the top, picking up four crew on the way.
You can't pass clocks that have struck midnight! Tick, tock!

MORE THINGS TO FIND

- Three clocks with their numbers in the wrong order
- A clock that says 5 o'clock
- A clock with a number missing

STAR GAZE DAZE

Pair up any stars with pictures that seem similar and then spot the three difference between each pair. It's extra eye-boggling!

MORE THINGS TO DO

✳ Wenda loves space music. Can you find nine stars in the shape of notes?

MOON MAYHEM

Help stop the hullabaloo on Planet Red and Blue! Find the words in the moon of letters – the words go up, down, forwards and backwards.

WORMHOLE
SUNSPOT
JETPACK
DUST
FULL MOON
NOVA

ORBIT
SPACESUIT
ROBOT
VOYAGER
CRATER
PULSAR

OUT OF THIS WORLD

Transform me and my friends into marvellous martians using a choice of wild and wacky colours!

SATELLITE SETS

Phew, it's crowded up here at night! Can you match each object in the sky with one or more identical copies – and reveal the one thing that is flying solo?

MORE THINGS TO FIND

- [ ] Six yellow cars
- [ ] Two fish
- [ ] Six thermometers
- [ ] Eighteen stripy planets
- [ ] Two spanners

THE PLANET HOP

Hop from planet to planet in this crazy race game to play with a friend!

START

START

HOW TO PLAY

- Use your finger to follow each move. No need to use a counter!
- One player starts on Wally, and moves from red planet to red planet, one planet at a time.
- The other player starts on Odlaw, and moves from yellow planet to yellow planet, one planet at a time.
- At each turn, move in a straight line (up, down, left and right).
- If your path is blocked, retrace your steps and find a new route!
- The winner is the first player to get to a planet next to their opponent's starting square.

MAKING CONTACT

Wow! The red planet is full of all sorts of secrets!
Use the decoder to read the magic messages.

A
B
C
D
E
F
G
H
I
J
K
L
M
N
O
P
Q
R
S
T
U
V
W
X
Y
Z

THERE ARE
THIRTY SIX RED
ALIENS IN THIS BOOK.
HELP ME FIND
THEM ALL!

WELL DONE, WALLY-WATCHERS!
DID YOU FIND THE PRECIOUS STAR?
IF NOT, THERE'S STILL TIME TO
SEARCH FOR IT!

WAIT, THERE'S MORE! LOOK BACK
THROUGH THE PICTURES TO FIND THE
ITEMS ON THE CHECKLIST AND SHOWN
IN THE STRIPY CIRCLES BELOW.

WISHING YOU THE LUCK OF
A THOUSAND STARS!

Wally

IN OUTER SPACE CHECKLIST

- [ ] An alien with two heads
- [ ] A knife and fork
- [ ] An upside-down clock
- [ ] A green alien pointing
- [ ] Four pyramids
- [ ] A red book being read
- [ ] A pink alien with four legs
- [ ] A green man holding a silver shield
- [ ] Wally writing with a pencil
- [ ] Thirteen green men on a bridge
- [ ] Two space dogs (find these on the cover)
- [ ] An aeroplane not leaving a trail
- [ ] Fourteen man-shaped silhouettes
- [ ] Six bear star constellations
- [ ] A ship
- [ ] A green alien with a pink nose
- [ ] Four Wally-watchers
- [ ] Thirty-two milk bottles
- [ ] A red-and-white umbrella
- [ ] An astronaut wearing pink boots
- [ ] A three-eyed cat

HERE ARE SOME ANSWERS TO THE HARDEST PUZZLES. DON'T GIVE UP ON THE OTHERS — WHY NOT ASK YOUR FRIENDS TO HELP?

WANDERING LINES

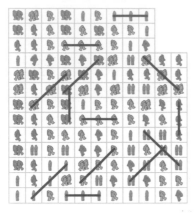

WORD WORLDS

1. Extraterrestrial 2. Universe 3. Space 4. Moon
5. Satellite 6. Astronaut 7. Mars 8. Sun 9. Twinkle
10. Telescope 11. Comet 12. Milky Way

TELEPORTATION TANGLE

TIME AND SPACE MAZE

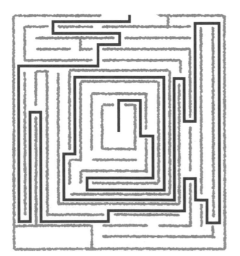

MAKING CONTACT

Top: There are thirty-six red aliens in this book. Help me find them all! Middle: See if you can also spot a planet with seven red aliens standing on it. Bottom: Locate five red-hooded monks spurting fire. I'm in my favourite coloured spaceship on that page.

MOON MAYHEM

First published 2016 by Walker Books Ltd, 87 Vauxhall Walk, London SE11 5HJ • 2 4 6 8 10 9 7 5 3 1 • © 1987–2016 Martin Handford • The right of Martin Handford to be identified as author/illustrator of this work has been asserted by him in accordance with the Copyright, Designs and Patents Act 1988. • This book has been typeset in Wallyfont and Optima • Printed in China • All rights reserved. • British Library Cataloguing in Publication Data: a catalogue record for this book is available from the British Library. • ISBN 978-1-4063-6820-8 • www.walker.co.uk

ONE LAST THING...
Did you spot a Wally star with a red-and-white striped tail and an Odlaw star with a yellow-and-black striped tail? Happy hunting!